Listening in on the Orchestra

by Tim Young
illustrated by Alexandra Colombo

Harcourt
SCHOOL PUBLISHERS

Printed in China

ISBN 10: 0-15-350497-8
ISBN 13: 978-0-15-350497-6

Ordering Options
ISBN 10: 0-15-350333-5 (Grade 3 Below-Level Collection)
ISBN 13: 978-0-15-350333-7 (Grade 3 Below-Level Collection)
ISBN 10: 0-15-357484-4 (package of 5)
ISBN 13: 978-0-15-357484-9 (package of 5)

4 5 6 7 8 9 10 0940 12 11 10 09

Characters

Taylor   **Stephen**   **Lauren**
Charlie   **Diana**   **Emily**

Setting: A concert hall

Taylor: Today we're visiting with members of the Lynnville Symphony Orchestra.

Lauren: Diana Nicholls is the orchestra's conductor. Diana, how did you become a conductor?

3

Diana: I studied the violin in college. As part of my training I took a conducting class. I wasn't sure about the class. To my surprise, I loved it.

Taylor: Tell us what you do as a conductor.

Diana: I lead the orchestra. I tell the musicians when to play faster and when to slow down. I tell them when it's time to make an enormous, heroic sound. I show them when to play with a soft, tender voice.

Lauren: How do you prepare the music for a concert?

Diana: First, I immerse myself in the score. A score shows the music for all the instruments in the orchestra. I think about how all the parts should sound.

Taylor: That's quite a burden for one person!

Diana: Not really. You learn to hear all the parts at once. You can hear quite a glorious concert in your mind!

Lauren: What are rehearsals like?

Diana: I'll let Stephen answer that. He's our first violinist. It's his job to help with rehearsals.

Stephen: Thanks! It's easy to rehearse with Diana. She listens to the musicians. You can have a dialogue with her. That doesn't happen with all conductors.

Diana: I like to listen to the musicians. They have great ideas. We'll try different ways to play a piece. One of their ideas may sound the best.

Stephen: Diana doesn't criticize us as long as we work hard. However, being on time is mandatory. If you're late, you're in trouble!

Charlie: That's for sure!

Taylor: Charlie, you're the percussionist. Tell us what you do.

Charlie: I'd be delighted. Percussion is more than drums. It includes any instrument that's struck, or hit. That means bells, the triangle, the xylophone, even blocks of wood!

Lauren: You must be busy!

Charlie: It can get crazy sometimes.
A good percussionist needs more than a
sense of rhythm. You need to stay focused.
You have to be able to juggle different jobs.
It's fun, though!

Taylor: Emily, you're the orchestra's newest member. Can you tell us how you got here?

Emily: I graduated from music school last year. I played my French horn in many performances, but I didn't have a full-time job. When I heard there was an opening for a French horn player, I auditioned, or tried out.

Lauren: What was that like?

Emily: It was scary! I didn't think I played my best. I was sure I'd ruined my chance. I got the job, though. It's been great. All the other musicians are so nice.

Taylor: In conclusion, what advice do you have for kids interested in music?

Diana: Listen to all kinds of music.

Emily: Find the instrument that is right for you.

Stephen: Practice!

Charlie: Have fun!

Lauren: Thanks! We can't wait to come hear you play!

Think Critically

1. How is the conductor's job different from the jobs of the musicians?

2. What is the theme of this play?

3. How would you describe Diana, the conductor?

4. What do percussionists do?

5. What musical instrument would you like to play? Why?

 **Drama**

Sound Off! Think about a song or piece of music you like. Write some words that describe how the music makes you feel. Then think of a way to act out each word.

School-Home Connection Talk about music with a family member. Discuss what kinds of music you each like and why.